MOZART
Sonatas for Pianoforte

Edited by
STANLEY SADIE

Fingering and performance notes by
DENIS MATTHEWS

THE ASSOCIATED BOARD OF
THE ROYAL SCHOOLS OF MUSIC

SONATA in C, K330/300*h*

In his editorial preface Dr Sadie has indicated that K330, like its companions K331 and K332, is now assigned to a later date in the light of recent research. For years it has been accepted as one of the sonatas Mozart composed on his visit to Paris in 1778 and about which he wrote to his father. Not so long ago H. Dennerlein, in his study *Der unbekannte Mozart* of 1951, claimed that it was the written-down version of the sonata that Mozart played 'out of his head' in Augsburg on his way to Mannheim and Paris. Others assumed that this improvised work rubbed off, as it were, on the sonata (also C major, K309) that he wrote on arrival in Mannheim for the young player, Rosa Cannabich, though its slow movement – a portrait of Rosa – was presumably new or at least reworked. In any case Mozart wrote that his spontaneous Augsburg sonata ended with a rondo, which fits K309 but rules out K330. If the news that K330 and its neighbours came later than imagined, in fact after Mozart's move to Vienna, causes players to look at them afresh and in a different context, so much the better. All are favourite sonatas and therefore well-worn by examination candidates as well as recitalists. Aubyn Raymar, a previous Associated Board editor, found K330 not so interesting. It is up to the performer, as spokesman for the defence, to disprove this; and he or she may find it helpful to view the whole sonata from the standpoint of the slow movement, which is one of the most touching pieces in all Mozart's solo piano works.

1   The added word 'moderato' should be a safeguard against playing this movement too fast. Think ahead to the prevalent demisemiquaver movement, which appears early and has melodic importance at b.42 and, with the technical hurdle of the trills, at b.129. With this thought in mind the opening r.h. theme will have air between the repeated notes, enabling the variant in b.3 to give emphasis to both semiquavers. The tempo in fact hovers on the border between two and four-in-a-bar, and this awareness will help those places where the harmony moves in quavers, as in b.13 and b.26. The addition of the many dynamic marks from the 1784 Artaria edition should be a great help in bringing the text to life, but the contrasts between *f* and *p* should not be overdone on a modern piano or prevent b.1 to b.18 unfolding as a single paragraph. The marks, however, look and sound authentic – see Mozart's letter to his father of 9–12 June 1784 – and it is valuable to contrast their musical purpose with the spurious accretions in many editions. The l.h. is light and buoyant even in *f* (hence the fingering suggested at the start), and the character of the whole movement is enhanced by Mozart's sparing use of an Alberti bass, e.g. b.20 and b.42.

Pedal should also be sparing, even in the more warmly expressive development, which begins (b.59) in a new episodic vein and is beautifully rounded up at the end of the movement. It is easy to mask the true melodic line in bb.62-3, where the E to F♯ interval is *legato* with no overlap. The E♮'s in b.63 are a presage of the minor-key events to come, and note Mozart's craft in recalling the figures of b.13 in C minor at b.81, as though preparing for the return and denying it at the same time. In the recapitulation the variants in b.92 and b.96 are best played with an element of witty surprise. A note on ornaments: the trill in b.2 may take in the demisemiquavers as part of its final flourish, or stop in advance of them – in which case the melodic-rhythmic figure will tie up with b.16 and even, subtly and at long distance, with the opening of the finale. Only the player can decide.

2   Anyone who is not profoundly moved by this movement had better not play it. The song-like character continues with an unbroken line even when the texture changes, as with the l.h. octave passages. The harmonic moves at b.9 and halfway through b.14 call for the utmost tenderness of expression, but the rhythmic element in b.17, reflected in the inner voice of b.18, should remove any trace of sentimentality. This dotted rhythm should never be played as a triplet. The upbeat quavers relate this theme to the F minor interlude at b.21. Pedal should not prolong the low bass-notes in the l.h., which is like a cello part in a quartet. From b.32, however, a duo takes over, and the quaver rests in each part are important. This middle section has its own coda and Mozart added a memory of it to form a coda to the whole movement. Both are tests of a player's harmonic response: to the poignancy of the dissonance in b.39, and to the consoling effect of the B♮'s in b.62.

3   The finale is obviously lightweight and brisker in tempo than the two-four of the first movement, though in this case triplets should be thought of in advance: b.16, b.29 and, more extended, from b.47 onwards. It is in sonata-form, not rondo, though the compact nature of the opening theme might lead one to expect the latter – in which case b.69 comes as a surprise: a new theme, and minor-key leanings from b.87 that recall the first movement at the same point. The counterstatement of the opening theme (b.9) has a solo-tutti antiphony, and the transition theme at b.21 bears a striking resemblance to one in the finale of the 'little' A major Concerto, K414. That also dates from 1782, the newly assigned date of the sonata – but it is easy to be wise after the event.

D.M.

Abbreviations in Textual Notes
cf. – *confer* [compare]; dsq – demisemiquaver; edn – edition; K – no. in Köchel catalogue of Mozart's works (no. before / is original no., no. after is that in 6th edn, 1964); LH – left hand; movt – movement; q – quaver; RH – right hand; sq – semiquaver; stacc. – staccato

Pitch – *c'* is middle C, *d'* the note above, *b* the note below; *c''* and *c'''* one and two octaves above, *c*, *C* and *C'* one, two and three octaves below

Numerals – arabic numerals in roman normally denote bar nos.; arabic in italic denote note nos. within the bar, counting left to right, chords downwards, and including all grace notes as notated

TEXTUAL NOTES

Composition   Munich or Vienna, 1781–3

Sources   autograph (formerly in Preussische Staatsbibliothek, Berlin) [A]; first edition, as no.1 of *Trois sonates pour le clavecin ou pianoforte composèes par W.A. Mozart. Oeuvre VI* (Vienna: Artaria, 1784) (nos.2 and 3 are K331/300*i* and 332/300*k*) [E]

Notes   There are many discrepancies between A and E in slurring, dynamic marks etc. The text here draws on both, but generally reckoning E as more nearly definitive in that it represents a later version prepared for publication (possibly by Mozart himself, or at least under his supervision). E, however, has many characteristic engraving errors and ambiguities, and A, coming direct from Mozart with no intermediary stage, often provides clarification as to his intentions. Dynamic indications from E alone are listed below, as are any discrepancies that might be significant. The exemplar of E used here, from the collection of Dr Alan Tyson, is of the very rare first impression (not to my knowledge used hitherto in an edition of these sonatas); many of the printing plates were evidently damaged and were replaced for later impressions by freshly engraved ones, which have several errors and omissions.

In this and the two succeeding sonatas, the autograph RH is written in the soprano clef; it is not known why Mozart departed from his usual practice in this way. High LH passages (those in the treble clef in the present edn) are also notated in the soprano clef.

1st movt   dynamic marks from E in the following bars: 5–30, 32, 36, 40–53, 59, 64–117, 119, 127–40, 149–50

bar	
13	E, LH stacc. lacking (also 15, except 2nd chord, 100, 102)
16	E, RH slurs *1–3*, *4–7*
26,28	E, RH slurs *2–4*
36	E, LH *d'* q
42	E, RH slur extends to 43, *1* (carelessly drawn in A, but meaning clear)
46–7	A, LH bass clef omitted
55	A, RH last slur lacking
66	E, LH slur to (?)67, *1*
100,102	see 13
116	A, RH slur to 117, *1*
130	E, RH slurs *3–5*, *6–9*, *10–13*; A originally thus too, but overwritten with slurs partly joined
131–2	E, RH stacc. 131, *6* and 132, *1*
134	E, LH 1st chord *f–a–c'*
135–6	E, RH 1 slur to each q; A ambiguous, possibly 2nd and 3rd qs together, 4th separate, but overlapping
135–7	A, RH slur to 136, *1* (and in 136 to 137, *1*); modified, and stacc. added to 136, *1* and 137, *1* by analogy (stacc. in E on 136, *1* only)

2nd movt   dynamic marks from E, 16, 17 (1st beat), 30, 35; last four bars lacking in A, presumably added by Mozart for publication – it is clear from A that the four-bar passage 36–40 was an earlier afterthought

bar	
10–11	A, RH slur lacking (also 50–51)
12	E, RH *f* halfway through 12 rather than at start of 13
40–60	A not written out: 'Da capo maggiore senza repliche'

3rd movt   all dynamic marks from E (A has none)

bar	
1	A, RH ?stacc. on *d"* (unclear)
22	E, *p* on 3rd q (also 117)
32	A, RH slur only *1–2*
63	A, RH, additional slur across whole bar to 64, *1*
67	A, LH, *b–g'* crotchet 1st beat (following original rejected text, 61–6)
77–91	A, LH slurs lacking
96–123	A not written out: 'Da Capo 28 täckt'
117	see 22
124ff	E, some LH slurs cover only 1st 3 notes (especially in 125–7); none in A, 124–9
162	A, RH slurs *1–2* and over entire bar; E, *1–2*, *2–5*

Editorial notes

In the printing of the text a distinction has been made between original and editorial markings. Slurs and ties added editorially are indicated by a small perpendicular stroke; editorial staccato marks (whether dots or wedges), dynamic markings and accidentals are indicated by the use of smaller type.

Editorial realizations of ornaments are shown in small notes above the text at the first occurrence of the ornament concerned in each movement. These realizations are based on the leading sources contemporary with Mozart, such as C. P. E. Bach's *Versuch über das wahre Art das Clavier zu spielen* (1753–62), Leopold Mozart's *Versuch einer gründlichen Violinschule* (1756) and Daniel Gottlob Türk's *Clavierschule* (1789). Our suggestions should not be taken as mandatory; any proper realization must take account of the tempo chosen for the movement concerned and the player's capabilities, and in a trill a player should feel free to play more notes, or fewer, as seems right. No ornament that feels awkward to the player, or sounds clumsy, is being satisfactorily realized. A player who wants to vary the realization of ornaments more extensively, however, would be well advised first to consult the writings of contemporary authorities, or failing that a summary of their views in a good modern reference work; he should note that except in very rare circumstances a trill should begin on the upper note in music of this period.

SONATA in C

Allegro moderato

K 330/300h (c. 1781)

Andante cantabile

Allegretto

Printed in England by Caligraving Limited Thetford Norfolk

A.B.1690

11:91

A|B|R|S|M
PUBLISHING

**The Associated Board of
the Royal Schools of Music
(Publishing) Limited**

14 Bedford Square
London WC1B 3JG

ISBN 1-85472-171-2

9 781854 721716